BIBLE STORIES

The Little Daughter
of Jairus

ILLUSTRATED BY STEPHANIE McFETRIDGE BRITT

First published in 1996 by Candle
Books. Distributed by SP Trust Ltd,
Triangle Business Park, Wendover
Road, Aylesbury, Bucks HP22 5BL,
England

ISBN 1 85985 101 0

Designed and created by
Three's Company,
5 Dryden Street,
London WC2E 9NW

Illustrations by Stephanie
McFetridge Britt

Worldwide co-edition organised and
produced by
Angus Hudson Ltd,
Concorde House,
Grenville Place,
London NW7 3SA
Phone +44 181 959 3668
Fax +44 181 959 3678

Printed in Singapore

The Little Daughter of Jairus

A little girl was watching for her father to come home. She lived in Capernaum, the town where Jesus often came.

'Where are you, Anna ?' called her mother.

The dark-eyed, dark-haired child called back: 'I am waiting for my father. He will play with me when he comes.'

Anna was twelve years old, an only child, and her parents loved her with all their hearts.

Each day when Jairus, her father, came home they played a game together. Anna always looked forward to that. Now she was watching for him as usual.

'Here he is!' she cried, and ran to meet the big man whose eyes and hair were so like hers. They played their game, and the mother heard them laughing and talking happily in the evening sunshine. She smiled happily too.

But none of them smiled the next day. Anna
fell ill.

'My head is hot,' she said. 'It hurts. I don't
want anything to eat. I don't want to play.'
Her father was suddenly anxious. 'Wife, the
child looks really ill,' he said. 'Put her to bed. I
will send for the doctor.'

So Anna was put to bed. The doctor came and
left her some medicine.

'She is no better,' said the mother that evening.
'We will send for the doctor again.'

The doctor was alarmed. 'I will get another
doctor,' he said. 'The child is very ill.'

In a day or two it was plain that Anna was terribly ill. Her father was in despair.

She is my only child, he kept thinking. *My dear, beloved little Anna. What can I do for her? The doctor has given up. I cannot let her die!*

He sat by the child's bedside. He looked at his anxious wife, pale and sad.

'Have you heard of this new healer, the man called Jesus?' he said suddenly. 'I think he is here, in the town.'

'Go and fetch him,' said his wife at once. 'He might come and lay his hand on our child and make her well. Go now, Jairus, before it is too late.'

'I will go and find him,' said Jairus. 'He is a good man and he loves little children. Surely he would come to our little Anna.'

Jairus made his way into the town and asked people anxiously where he could find Jesus. He went to the house where Jesus stayed – but he was not there!

'Go down to the lakeside,' said the woman who opened the door. 'He may be preaching there.'

So Jairus went down to the blue water, and there he saw a great crowd of people. 'Is Jesus here?' he asked. 'Where is he?'

'No, he is not here,' said someone. 'He was with us only last night, telling us stories from Peter's boat. Then he sailed off over the lake. A storm blew up later – we hope Jesus is safe. We are waiting for the boat to come back.'

'Will he be long?' asked Jairus, in despair.

But nobody knew.

So Jairus stood with the people and waited, straining his eyes to see across the lake. He thought of Anna, lying so ill. Was she still alive? Every minute mattered now. If only Jesus would come!

'There's a boat now,' said somebody. But it was not Peter's boat. Jairus's heart sank.

After a little while somebody shouted: 'I can see the boat. Look! Jesus is coming!'

The boat ran into the shore. Jesus sprang to the beach, and the disciples tried to keep back the people crowding round him.

'Let me through,' Jairus begged. 'Do let me through.'

The crowd opened to let him pass. They saw that he had something urgent to say to Jesus. Jairus knelt down in front of Jesus and begged him to come and see his little girl.

'She is at the point of death,' said Jairus, his voice trembling. 'I pray you, Lord, come and put your hands on her, that she may be healed.'

Jesus saw that Jairus was desperate. 'I will come at once,' he said. 'Let us go.'

The Woman in the Crowd

The crowd jostled and pressed round Jesus and the disciples as they went with Jairus.

Now, in the crowd, there was a poor, miserable woman. She was ill with a disease that no doctor seemed able to cure. For twelve years she had spent all her money on doctors, and now she was worse.

She had heard of Jesus, of course. *I would never dare to speak to him, or ask him to heal me,* she thought. *But suppose I got near enough just to touch the hem of his robe – why, that would be enough to make me well again!*

So, as Jesus was walking along with Jairus, this woman made her way closer and closer to him in the crowd. At last she was just behind him. With a beating heart she put out her hand and touched the bottom of his cloak.

No sooner had she touched it than her body felt strong and healthy. The woman was overcome with joy and wonder. Now she must get away and think of the marvellous thing that had happened to her.

But before she could go, Jesus stopped and looked round.

'Who touched me?' he asked.

'I didn't, Master,' said one near by.

'Nor did I,' said another.

Peter was astonished at Jesus' question.

'Master, what do you mean, who touched you?' he asked. 'Look at the crowd round you! Many people must have touched you.'

But Jesus knew quite well that someone had touched him on purpose, because he had felt goodness going out of him. Someone had wanted his help, and had got it without even asking for it. Who was it?

Jairus did not want to stop. *Oh, hurry, hurry!* he thought. *There is no time to be lost.*

The woman felt that Jesus was looking at her. She came forward and knelt down, trembling. She told him of her disease.

'I knew that if I touched just the hem of your cloak, I would be healed,' she said.

'Daughter,' said Jesus, gently, 'because you trusted me so much, you were healed. Go in peace.'

As the woman was slipping away, Jairus saw messengers pushing their way through the people. 'Where is Jairus?' they asked.

Jairus felt his heart go cold, for the faces of the messengers were sad.

'Sir,' said one. 'Do not trouble the Master now. Your little girl is dead.'

Jairus turned in despair to Jesus, tears in his eyes. It was too late after all!

Jesus spoke comfortingly to him. 'Don't be afraid. Only believe in me.'

He walked on with Jairus, and the crowd followed. When he came near the house Jesus turned and spoke to the people.

'Come no further,' he said. Then, taking James and Peter and John with him, he went into the house with Jairus.

As soon as they were inside they heard a great noise of weeping and wailing. In those days when anyone died people were paid to come and wail for the dead; already they were wailing for little Anna.

Jesus could not bear this noise. He knew that the people there had been paid to weep and wail; they were not weeping for Anna from their hearts.

'Why do you make this noise?' Jesus asked them. 'The little girl is not dead. She is asleep.'

Then they all laughed at him, for they had seen that the child was dead.

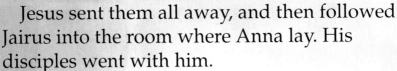

Jesus sent them all away, and then followed Jairus into the room where Anna lay. His disciples went with him.

The mother was there, weeping bitterly. 'You were too late, Jairus,' she sobbed. 'You did not even say good-bye to our poor little Anna.'

Jairus looked at her in despair, and then turned to Jesus. No one but Jesus could do anything now.

Jesus stood by the bed, looking at the child who lay so still. He put out his hand and took Anna's in his. He held it firmly in his warm hand.

'Get up, my child,' he said.

Anna opened her eyes. She sat up, looking all round. She was surprised to see so many people. She smiled at her father. Then she got up from her bed and walked a few steps.

Her mother and father could hardly believe their eyes. 'Anna!' said her mother. 'My little Anna.'

And in a moment she was in the arms of her father and mother. They kissed her and cuddled her, crying for joy. She was alive again!

Jesus watched them with gladness.

'Tell no one of this,' he said to Jairus.

Then he turned to Anna's mother. She was quite beside herself with joy. Jesus knew that he must give her something to do for her child.

'Give Anna something to eat,' he said. The mother went gladly to fetch some food.

Jesus went from the house, leaving behind a very happy family.

'I want to see that man again,' said Anna to her parents. 'He is kind. I like him.'

And so, when Jesus visited Capernaum, and the children came round him, little Anna was always there, waiting.

She listened to his stories, gazing up into his clear, steadfast eyes. She would do anything in the world for Jesus!